The Way of Silence

THE PROSE AND POETRY OF BASHO

Richard Lewis / *photographs by Helen Buttfield*

The Dial Press, New York

To Sascha,
who from gentle
silence came

To Karen – Who Sascha must be like.
Kit

...all who have achieved real excellence in any art possess one thing in common; that is, a mind to obey nature, to be one with nature, throughout the four seasons of the year. Whatever such a mind sees is a flower, and whatever such a mind dreams of is the moon. It is only a barbarous mind that sees other than the flower, merely an animal mind that dreams of other than the moon. The first lesson for the artist is, therefore, to learn how to overcome such barbarism and animality, to follow nature, to be one with nature.

Basho

Basho was born in 1644 in Iga-Ueno, Japan. For many years he studied the writing of haiku with the son of the local lord. At the age of twenty-nine he moved to Edo (Tokyo), where he composed haiku mostly of a humorous nature. In 1680 he went to the outskirts of Edo and lived in a small hut. After 1684 Basho's poetry took on a new character reflecting a highly original departure from the lightness of traditional haiku writing. At about this same time he also began taking many journeys throughout Japan, traveling simply and recording his impressions in prose and poetry in private journals. He died in 1694.

His work and his life subsequently became models for many poets, including such masters as Issa and Buson. He is rightly credited with having transformed the haiku poem into a serious expressive form and is one of its finest practitioners in the history of Japanese literature.

Ideally this book should be read as an uninterrupted narrative of Basho's quest for truth. The text has been arranged so that the reader may be able to experience not only Basho's thoughts and impressions through his prose writings, but the realization of these writings in his haiku poetry. The book is in no way meant to be an exact recreation of his life. Instead, it is a broad interpretation in the form of a journey similar to the journeys Basho took in his later years.

The manner in which Basho speaks to us is deceptively simple. On the surface we see a poet wandering through seasons and landscapes, who gradually withdraws from human contact and enters into solitary communion with nature. But beneath the surface, we discover a man using all his imaginative and spiritual powers in order, as R. H. Blyth has said, "to get into the deepest possible contact with the greatest number of things." It was this striving for contact with the very center of life that enabled Basho to communicate something of what has been referred to as the "eternal beyond," where there is no beginning and no end.

Traveling with the seasons, Basho sought solitude not just to be alone but to observe the most minute aspects of nature as if they were an extension of himself. In his poetry he constantly made an attempt to give permanence to that moment in which he and nature had become one. The world for Basho was never static but an ever-evolving state in which poetry and life were synonymous.

In our own time man's preoccupations have become distant from nature. We deem other things more important than the communications of the moment. Energy and speed dominate us. Aloneness and silence are unacceptable.

And perhaps for these very reasons, the work of Basho comes alive now with a special poignancy. For he, having sought the "hidden glimmering" in all things, awakens, through his poetry, that power of observation and expression inherent in man's imagination. And speaking in solitude he reached out to align his spirit once again with its original source in nature. Basho not only contributed significantly to world literature—he discovered a road whose direction will continue to lead us to profound and necessary pathways.

R.L.
April, 1970

Days and months are travellers of eternity. So are the years that pass by. Those who steer a boat across the sea, or drive a horse over the earth till they succumb to the weight of years, spend every minute of their lives travelling. There are a great number of ancients, too, who have died on the road. I myself have been tempted for a long time by the cloud-moving wind—filled with a strong desire to wander.

Suddenly the sun rose,
To the scent of the plum blossoms
Along the mountain path.

Ah, it is spring,
Great spring it is now,
Great, great spring—
Ah, great—

The spirits of the road beckoned, and I could do
no work at all.

On horseback, half-asleep
Half-dreaming
　　Smoke for the morning tea.

In the midst of the plain
Sings the skylark,
Free of all things.

Every turn of the road brought me new thoughts,
and every sunrise gave me fresh emotions.

On the point of scooping up the water,
I felt it in my teeth—
The water of the spring.

Summer in the world;
Floating on the waves
Of the lake.

The tree does bear flowers, but unlike other flowers, there is nothing gay about them. The big trunk of the tree is untouched by the axe, for it is utterly useless as building wood. I love the tree, however, for its very uselessness. . . . I sit underneath it and enjoy the wind and rain that blow against it.

Not knowing
The name of the tree,
I stood in the flood
Of its sweet smell.

The beautiful scene was silent and still; my heart was at rest.
I was conscious only of this.

Summer grass
Where warriors dream.

It was not yet dark when we arranged to spend the night at the foot of the hill, and we climbed up to the main temple. The hill was all boulders one upon another, the pine trees and cypresses ancient, earth and stones old and mossy, the temples with doors closed standing on the rocks, not a sound to be heard. We crept over or round the rocks and worshipped at the temples, our hearts filled with the mysterious silence and wonderful scenery.

The god is absent;
His dead leaves are piling,
And all is deserted.

Just at this time, however, moonlight touched the corner of my room, coming
through the hanging leaves and the chinks in the wall. As I bent my ears
to the noise of wooden clappers and the voices of the villagers chasing wild
deer away, I felt in my heart that the loneliness of autumn was now
consummated . . .

The moon about to appear,
All present tonight
        With their hands on their knees.

Plates and bowls,
Faintly through the twilight,
    In the evening cool.

The peaks of clouds
Have crumbled into fragments—
The moonlit mountain.

Clouds now and then
Giving men relief
From moon viewing.

At midnight
Under the bright moon,
A secret worm
Digs into a chestnut.

Shortly before daybreak, the moon began to shine through the rifts made in the hanging clouds. I immediately wakened the priest, and other members of the household followed him out of bed. We sat for a long time in utter silence, watching the moonlight trying to penetrate the clouds and listening to the sound of the lingering rain.

The moon swiftly fleeting,
Branches still holding
The raindrops.

The voice of a cuckoo
Dropped to the lake
Where it lay floating
On the surface.

I walked through mists and clouds, breathing the thin air of high altitudes
and stepping on slippery ice and snow, till at last through a gateway of
clouds, as it seemed, to the very paths of the sun and moon, I reached the
summit, completely out of breath and nearly frozen to death.

Tell me the loneliness
Of this deserted mountain,
The aged farmer
Digging wild potatoes.

The green of the pines is of a wonderful darkness, and their branches are constantly bent by winds from the sea, so that their crookedness seems to belong to the nature of the trees. The scene suggests all the mysterious charm of a beautiful face.

From far and near,
Voices of waterfalls are heard,
Leaves falling.

What is important is to keep our mind high in the world of true understanding, and returning to the world of our daily experience to seek therein the truth of beauty. No matter what we may be doing at a given moment, we must not forget that it has a bearing upon our everlasting self, which is poetry.

Together let us eat
Ears of wheat,
Sharing at night
A grass pillow.

Sleeping on a journey—
Is some dog being rained on too?
The voices of night.

In the Month-when-the-gods-are-absent, the sky when I set out was
uncertain, myself a leaf blown by the wind, unmindful whither.

With what voice,
And what song would you sing, spider,
In this autumn breeze?

Above my head, mountains rose over mountains, and on my left a huge precipice dropped a thousand feet into a boiling river, leaving not a tiny square of flat land in between, so that, perched on the high saddle, I felt stricken with terror . . .

The first winter rain,
And my name shall be called,
        "Traveller."

Journeying through the world—
To and fro, to and fro,
        Harrowing the small field.

As firmly cemented clam shells
Fall apart in autumn,
So I must take to the road again,
Farewell, my friends.

Time passes and the world changes. The remains of the past are shrouded in uncertainty.

I roamed by the shores of the lake in quest of a place to stay, a single stalk of reed where the floating nest of the grebe might be borne to rest by the current.

Tall islands point to the sky and level ones prostrate themselves before the surges of water. Islands are piled above islands, and islands are joined to islands, so that they look exactly like parents caressing their children or walking with them arm in arm.

Where the cuckoo's voice
Glided into the sea
Shooting across the sky,
I found an island.

. . . I have decided to live in complete isolation with a firmly closed door. My solitude shall be my company, and my poverty my wealth.

A bowel-freezing night;
The sound of the oar striking the wave—
Tears.

Winter desolation;
In a world of one color
The sound of the wind.

The winter storm
Hid itself in the bamboos,
And grew still.

When we observe them calmly, we notice that all things have their fulfillment.

Season of spring days!
There a nameless hill has veils
Of soft morning haze.

Do not doubt it,
The bay has its spring too—
The flowers of the tide.

Ah, how glorious!
The young leaves, the green leaves
Glittering in the sunshine.

Once in a while, when I feel energetic, I gather firewood and dip spring water. I love the drops which fall tok-tok along the green of a single spray of fern, and nothing is so light as my stove.

I am one
Who eats his breakfast,
    Gazing at the morning glories.

      The moon has sunk below the horizon;
All that remains,
    The four corners of a table.

The Way of Haiku arises from concentration and lack of distraction.
Look well within yourself.

Quietness . . .
On the wall, where hangs a painting,
a grasshopper chirps.

A flower of the camellia tree
Fell,
Spilling its water.

. . . when, as very rarely happens, visitors come from afar, we sit calmly
at night, the moonlight our companion, arguing with our shadows.

At my hut,
All that I have to offer you,
Is that the mosquitoes are small.

In imagination,
An old woman and I
Sat together in tears
Admiring the moon.

In the sound of the frog leaping from the bank overgrown with wild grass, a haiku is heard. There is the seen; there is the heard. Where there is haiku as the poet has felt it, there is poetic truth.

The old pond;
A frog jumps in—
The sound of the water.

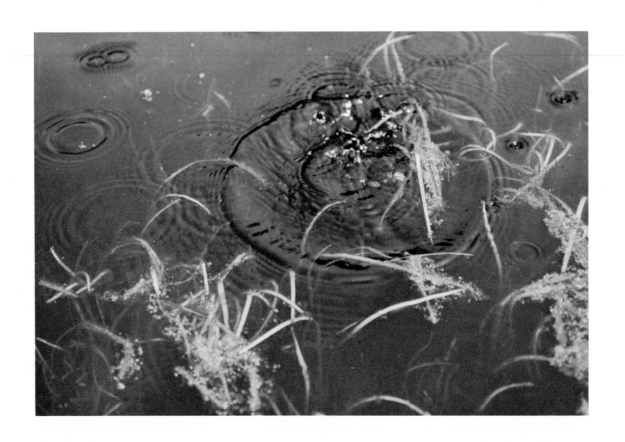

Your poetry issues of its own accord when you and the object have become one—when you have plunged deep enough into the object to see something like a hidden glimmering there.

The beginning of autumn;
The sea and fields,
    All one same green.

I do not seek to follow in the footsteps of the men of old;
I seek the things they sought.

The sun had already sunk into the sea, the moon darkly somber. The Silver
River stretched out over half the heavens, the stars flickering bright and
clear. From the offing, the sound of the waves was now and then carried
upward. Loneliness oppressed me; a grinding feeling of wretchedness,
a feeling as if my bowels were being torn asunder.

This autumn—
Old age I feel,
In the birds, the clouds.

My thatched hut;
In the world outside
Is it harvest time?

The dew falls drip-drop:
Would I could dip myself here
And wash away the world.

The sea darkens,
The cries of the seagulls
Are faintly white.

. . . I am like a sick man weary of people, or someone who is tired of the
world. What is there to say? . . . Ever since I was very young, I have been
fond of my eccentric ways, and once I had come to make them the source
of a livelihood, temporarily I thought, I discovered myself bound for life
to the one line of my art, incapable and talentless as I am. I labor without
results, am worn of spirit and wrinkled of brow. Now, when autumn is
half over, and every morning and each evening brings changes to the scene,
I wonder if that is not what is meant by dwelling in unreality.

The shell of a cicada;
It sang itself
Utterly away.

No sooner had I decided to give up my poetry and closed my mouth than
a sentiment tempted my heart and something flickered in my mind.
Such is the magic power of the poetic spirit.

Taken in my hand
It melts in the warmth of tears—
This autumn frost.

Failing health and strength;
My teeth grate
On the sand in the seaweed.

My body, now close to fifty years of age, has become an old tree that bears bitter peaches, a snail which has lost its shell, a bagworm separated from its bag; it drifts with the winds and clouds that know no destination.

Whitened bones in a field—
I see them now—at the thought
How the wind chills my flesh.

Yield to the willow
All the loathing, all the desire
Of your heart.

I sleep,
Making coolness
My lodging place.

Never forget
The lonely taste
Of the white dew.

I resemble a priest, but the dust
of the world is on me.

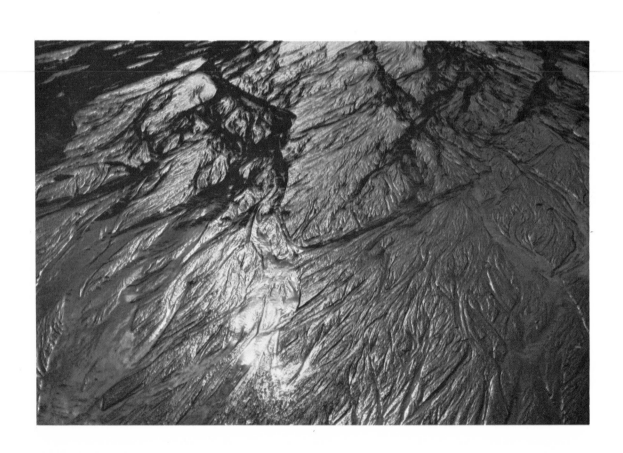

Still alive
At the end of the journey!
An evening of late autumn.

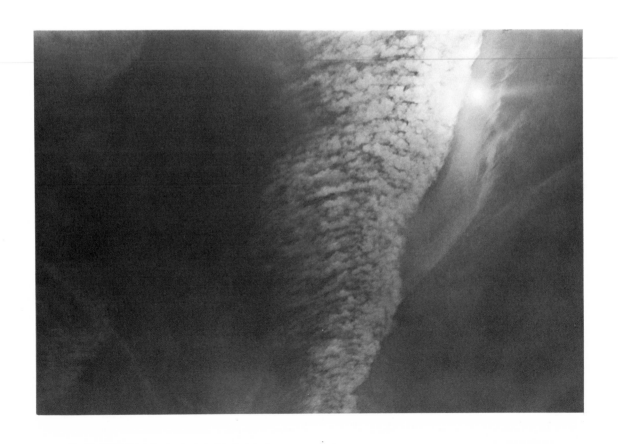

From old times it has been customary to leave behind a death poem, and perhaps I should do the same. But every moment of life is the last, every poem a death poem! Why then at this time should I write one? In these my last hours I have no poem.